Grand Canyon Diorama poster, Disneyland (1958). By Paul Hartley
Haunted Mansion poster, Disneyland (1969). By Ken Chapman and Marc Davis
World Bazaar poster, Tokyo Disneyland (2002). Adapted by Will Eyerman
from the 1983 version by Rudy Lord and Greg Paul
Alice in Wonderland poster, Disneyland (1958). By Sam McKim
Walt Disney World Monorail System (1971). Adapted by Collin Campbell
from the 1961 Disneyland Monorail version by Paul Hartley
Orbitron-Machines Volantes poster, Disneyland Paris (1991).
By Tim Delaney and Jim Michaelson
Cinderella Castle Mystery Tour poster, Tokyo Disneyland (1986).
By John Drury and Greg Paul
Disneyland Railroad poster, Disneyland (1977). By Jim Michaelson,
Ernie Prinzhorn and Rudy Lord

First published in the UK in 2023 by Studio Press,
an imprint of Bonnier Books UK,
4th Floor, Victoria House, Bloomsbury Square, London. WC1B 4DA
Owned by Bonnier Books,
Sveavägen 56, Stockholm, Sweden

bonnierbooks.co.uk

MIX
Paper | Supporting
responsible forestry
FSC® C104723

Printed in China
5 7 9 10 8 6 4

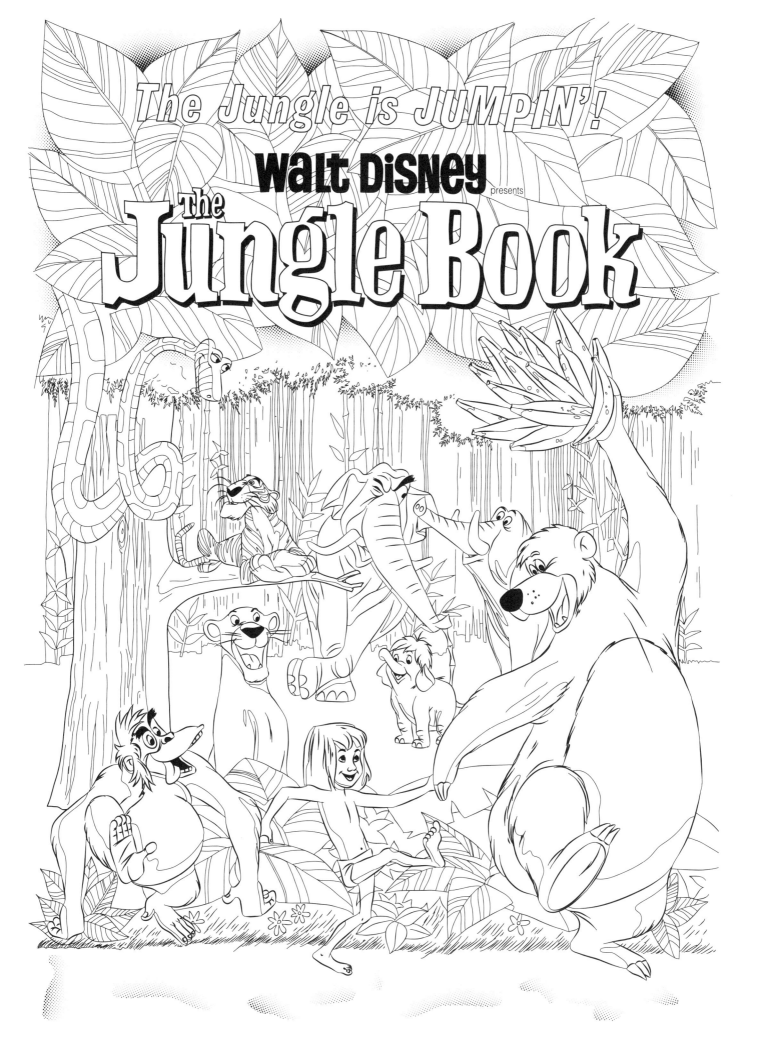

MICKEY MOUSE

in

FISHIN' AROUND

Produced by WALT DISNEY

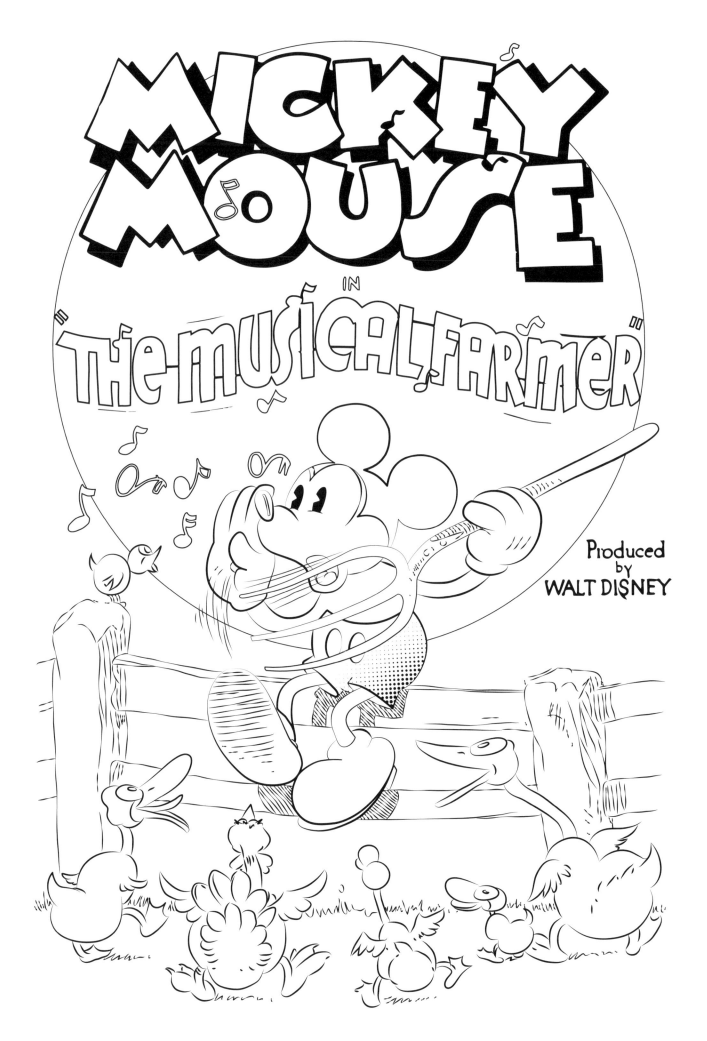

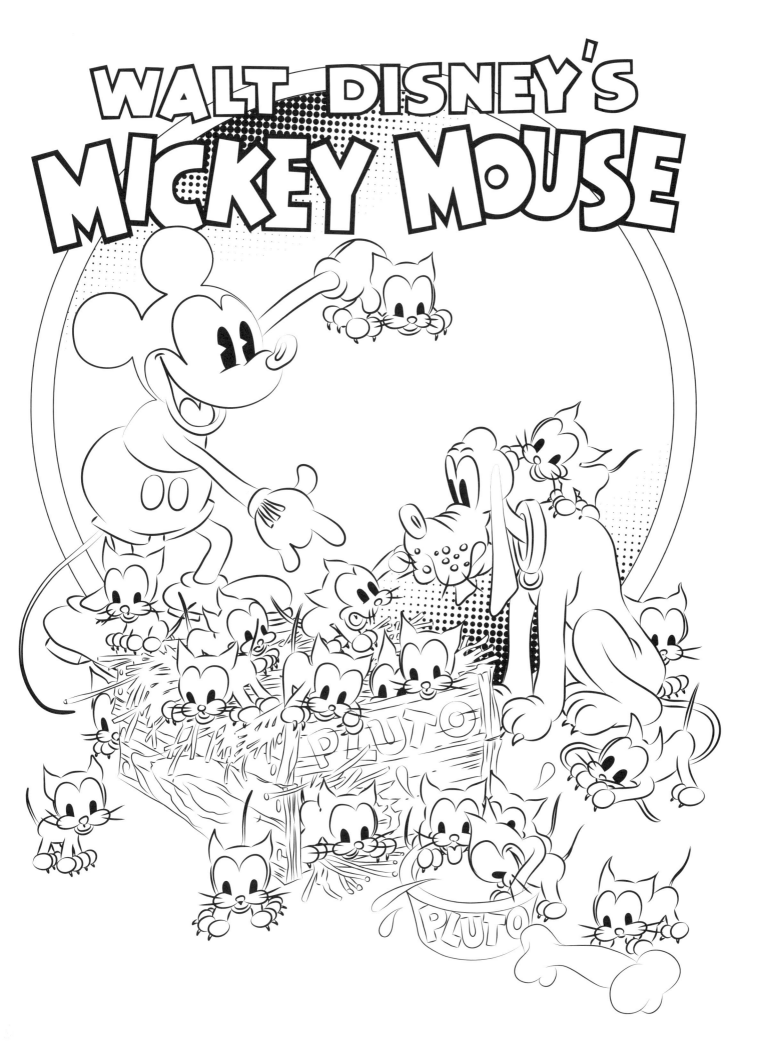

WALT DISNEY

HOW TO PLAY FOOTBALL

Walt Disney's

Snow White

and the Seven Dwarfs

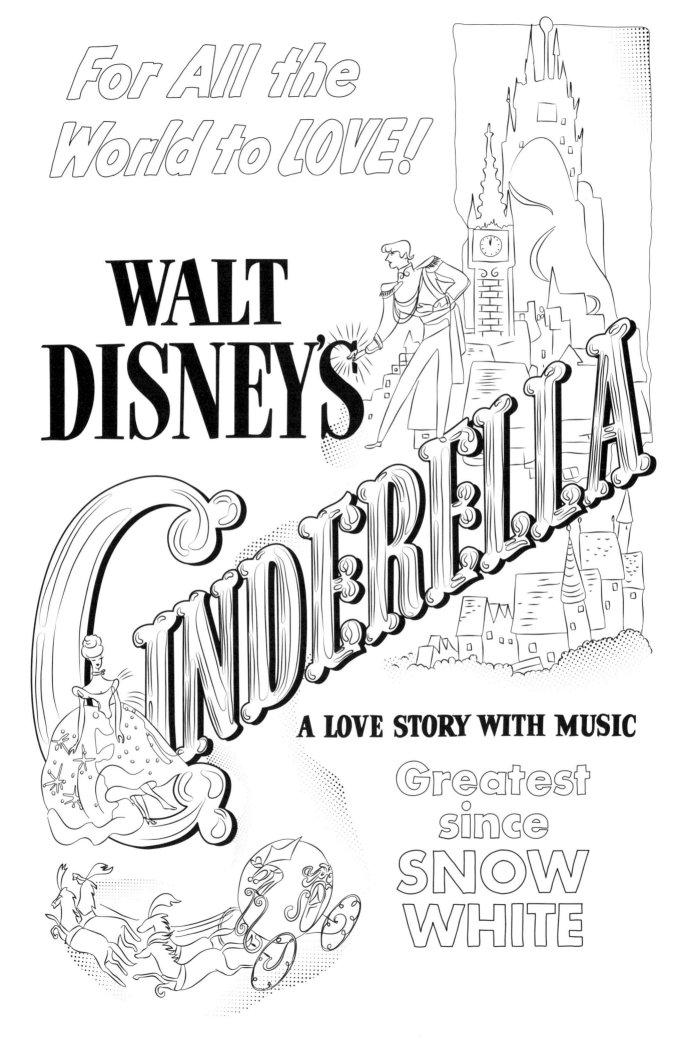

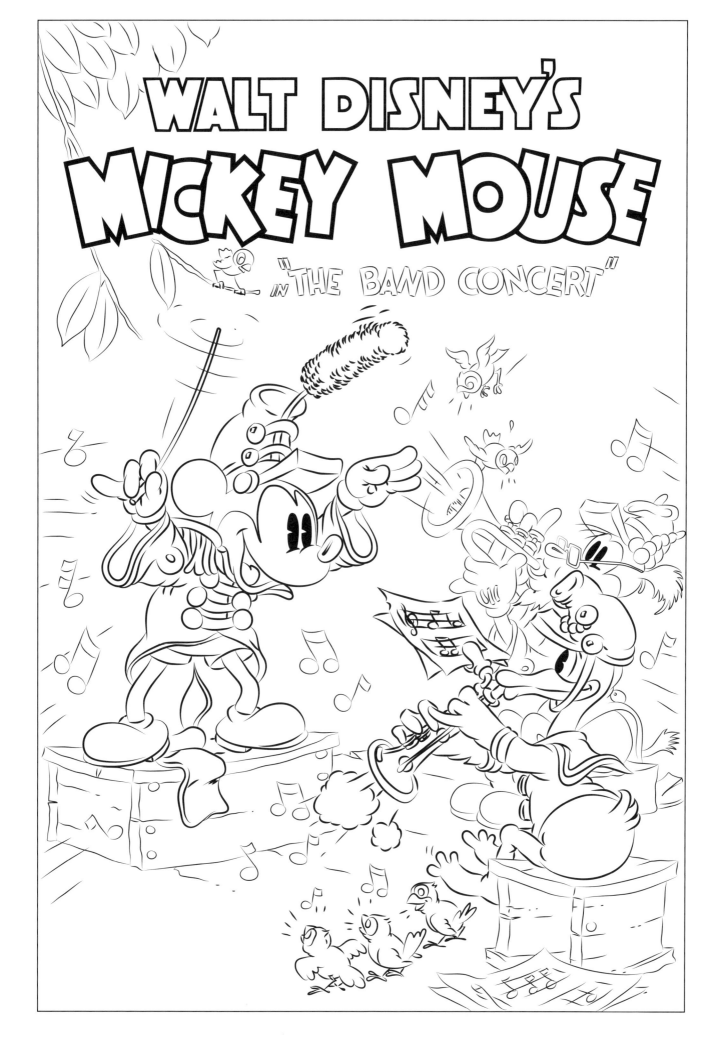

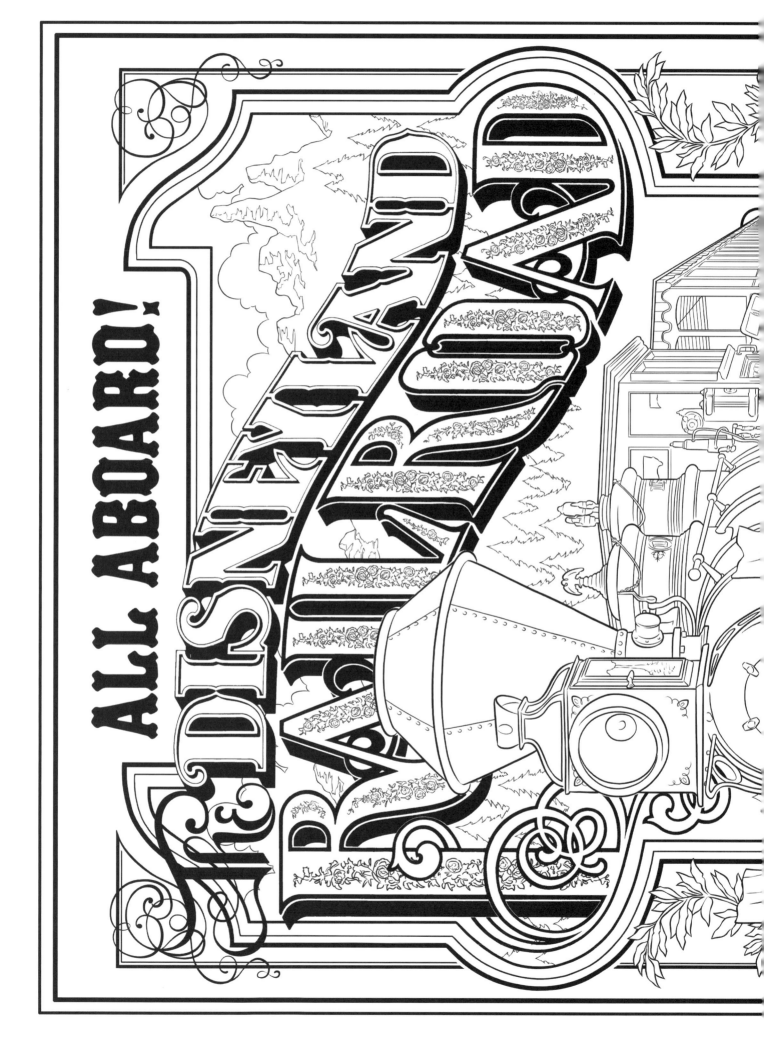

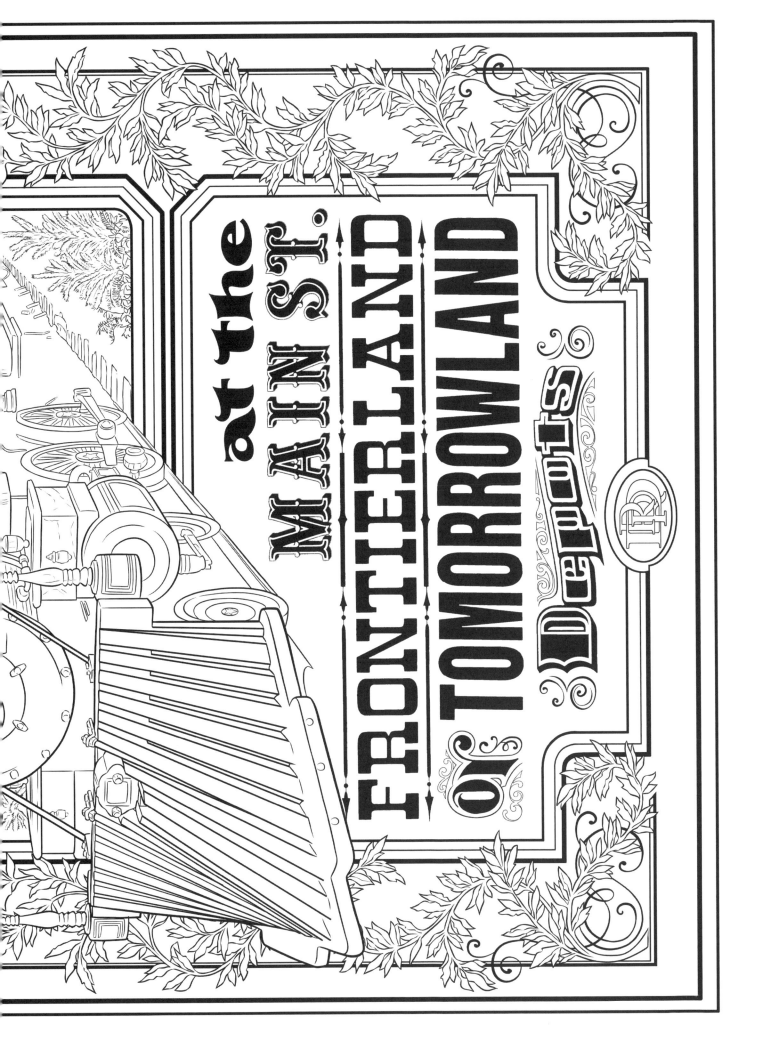

Clang! Clang! Here comes the boy in the red coat, dragging a load of laughs in his whizzing wagon! . . . One of the funniest yet. Watch for it at your favorite movie!

WALT DISNEY'S
Donald Duck
in FIRE CHIEF

FIRE
13
CHIEF

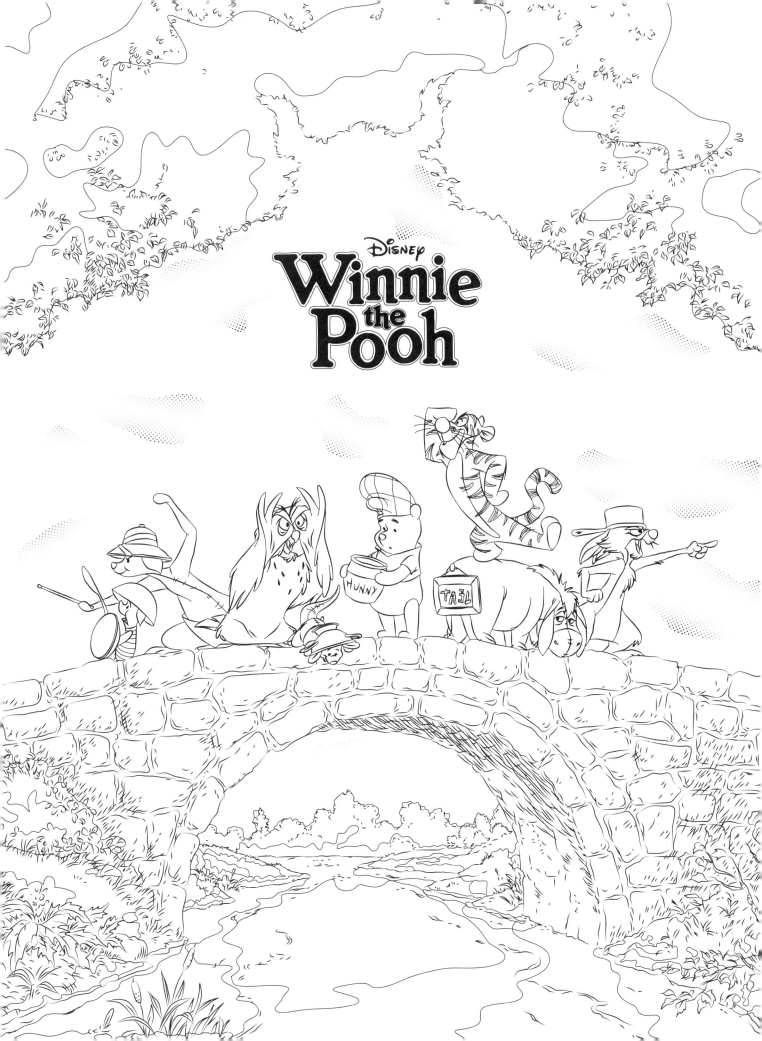

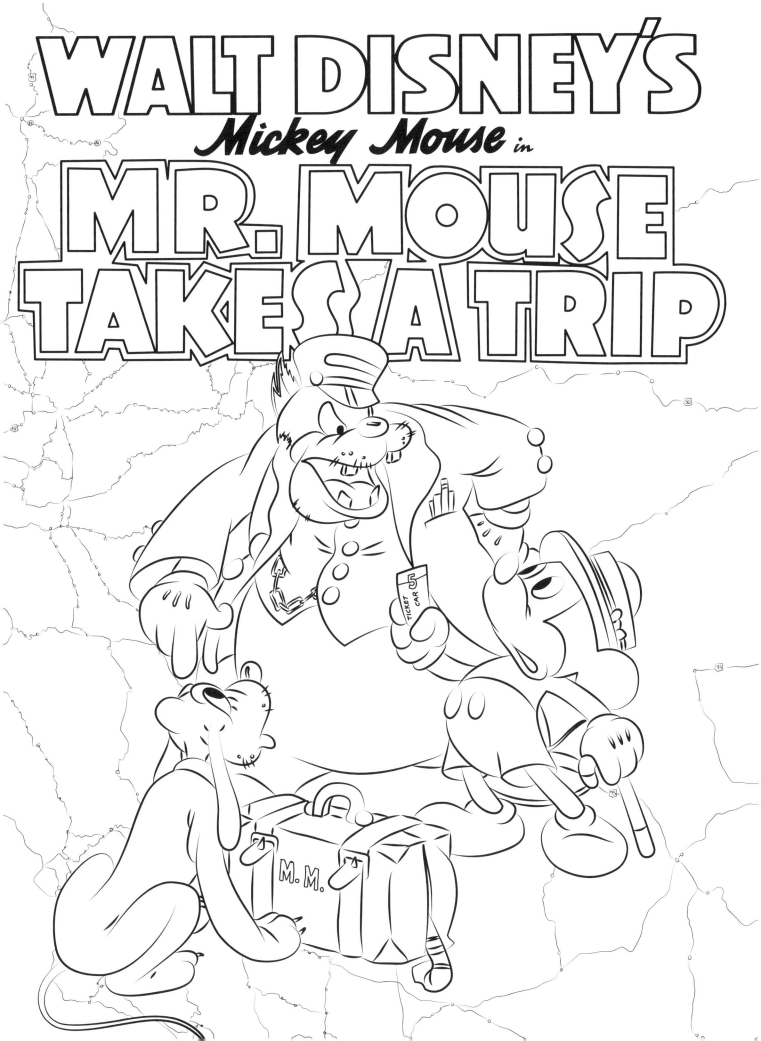

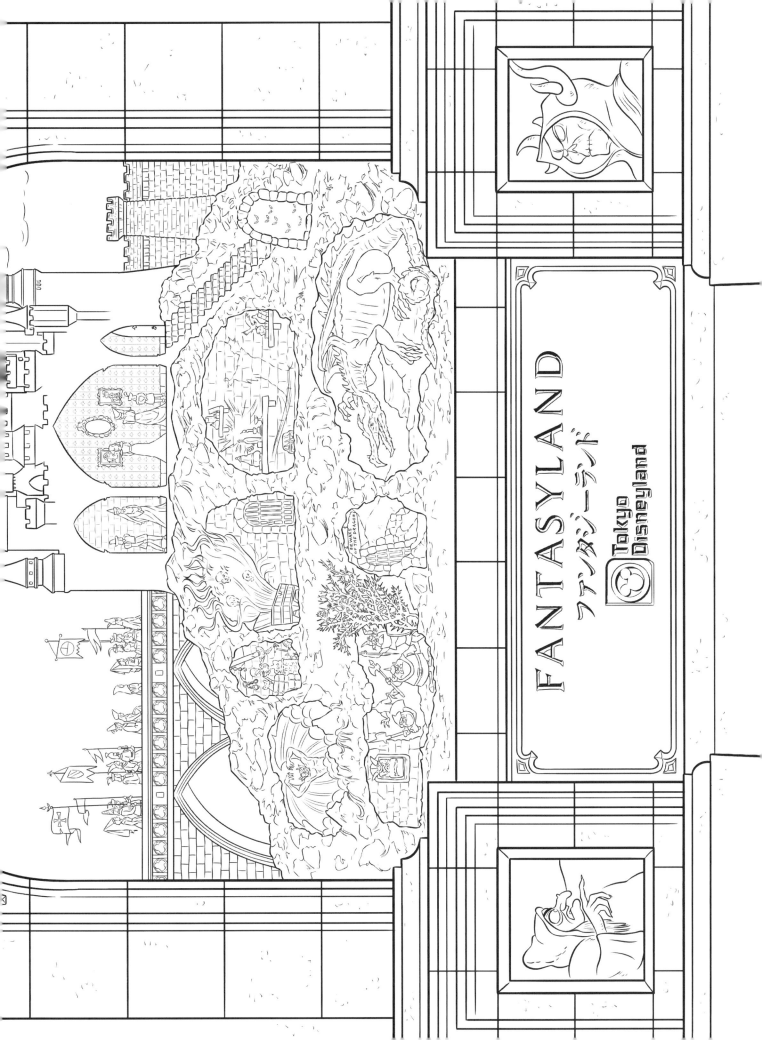

RIDE THE

SANTA FE & DISNEYLAND R.R.

THE SCENIC ROUTE AROUND DISNEYLAND

GRAND
CANYON

VIA

DIORAMA

LARGEST IN THE WORLD

DEPOTS ᜥᜥ MAIN ST. ~ FRONTIERLAND
ᜥᜥ AT ᜥᜥ AND TOMORROWLAND

WALT
DISNEY'S
Goofy

ONE GREAT BIG ONEDERFUL MOTION PICTURE

WALT DISNEY'S
NEW ALL-CARTOON FEATURE

One Hundred and One Dalmatians

WALT DISNEY WORLD

MONORAIL

SYSTEM

BOARD AT HOTELS
and MAIN ENTRANCE

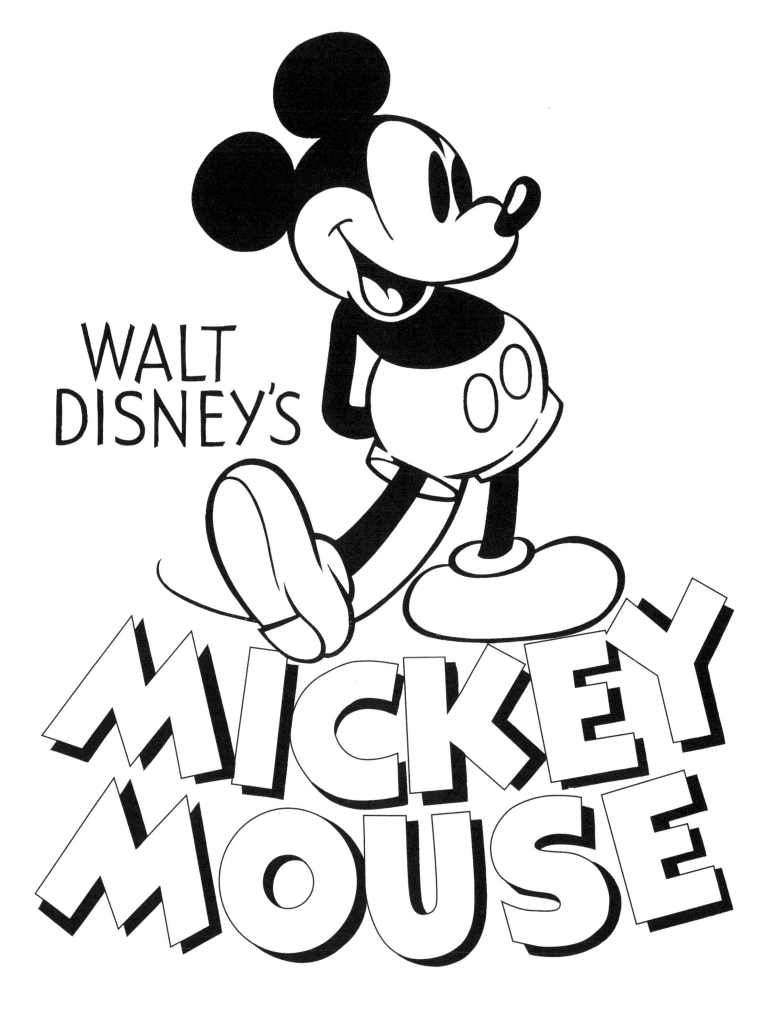